The Best *ME* That I Can Be
RESPECT

BY ROSE ANGEBRANDT

For Keigan and Ayzlin

You are loved more than words can say

My name is Keigan and I want to be

the Best **ME** that I Can BE!

I'm learning about **Respect**. What does

that mean?... Well... it's like this...

My Family are ***super cool*** and take

care of me. I love them lots!

My Teacher at School is ***awesome***! She helps me learn.

I think my Friends are s***o much fun***!

We play and laugh together.

My Family, Teacher and Friends are **ALL** very special to me. It is because they are *special* I want to show them the VERY best **ME** that I can be!

THIS is showing Respect.

I meet people every day. Some people are nice
and kind and help me. When I smile at them
they *always* smile back. I try to be polite to
them to show them I am a nice person too.

This is showing Respect for nice, kind and helpful people.

I love to play with my Friends. Sometimes we play together at the park and fly my *jazzy-colour long-tail* Kite. We run as *fast as the wind* to make it fly! I wait until each of my Friends have had a turn until I take my turn.

This is how I show Respect to my Friends.

I love going to School. My Teacher is Miss Holly and she is *really* smart. When Miss Holly starts to talk, I know that we should all be quiet and **listen** to what she is teaching us. This is how we **learn** lots of things.

This is also how we show Respect to Miss Holly for helping us learn.

I'm a better **ME** when I listen and learn. I was going to use some of Mommy's long *pretty fancy* Dresses for a backyard Tent. It was going to be *SUPER* cool! Mommy did not think using her Dresses would be that cool.

"ASK FIRST if you want to take something that doesn't belong to you."

Taking without asking is *NOT* showing Respect for Mommy.

I had worked hard to plan my *SUPER* cool Tent!
Mommy let me use some colourful Blankets instead
of her Dresses to make it. It was the best Tent *EVER*
and my Friends and I had so much fun playing in it! I
even made us a *super yummy* picnic lunch to eat.

I promised Mommy that I would give her back the Blankets when we were done playing with them.

To be the best **ME** that I can be, I always try to keep my promises.

Keeping promises is *also* showing Respect.

One *BIG* thing I am learning is that I should always listen to what Mommy tells me... like to *ASK FIRST*.

I know that everyone makes mistakes. I know when I have done something wrong it is best to go tell Mommy. She will know what to do.

I told Mommy I made a big mistake. For my *super yummy* picnic lunch I took a Cupcake that was in the fridge. It was *SOOOOO yummy good!*

I did not know this was a special Cupcake my sister Ayzlin bought with money she saved up for a long time. I did not *ASK FIRST*.

Now Ayzlin is crying and really sad. I know saying sorry when you have done something wrong is showing Respect. But... *THIS* is a really BIG wrong.

I didn't mean to make Ayzlin cry and be sad. I was wrong because I didn't *ASK FIRST* if I could eat the *SOOOOO yummy good* Cupcake.

Mommy hugged me and asked, *"Is there something you can do to make your wrong a right? Maybe you could replace her Cupcake? Can you think of a way you can do that?"*

I made a plan to make right what I had done wrong. It would have been easy to tell Ayzlin that I never even saw her *SOOOOO yummy good* Cupcake... *AND* that I never ate it! But that would not be honest or nice. That would be lying.

That would *NOT* be showing respect to Ayzlin.

I would ALSO *not* be showing respect for **ME**. I try to always do things right and be the best ME that I can be. This is called having Self-Respect. I should not do things that I know are wrong... like lying.

I have respect for **ME** too.

I'm learning that Respect is *BIG*. I can show Respect to nice, kind and helpful people by using my *VERY* best manners. I say Hello, Goodbye, Please and Thank-you.

Respect is not just what I *SAY* but also what I *DO*. I know that if someone is speaking to me, it is polite if I look at them and listen to what they are saying.

It's like listening to Mommy when she says to ASK *FIRST* before taking something *SOOOOO yummy good* or *pretty fancy*...even if I have a *SUPER* cool plan!

This is showing Respect and being my Best **ME** that I can be.

What do I know about **Respect**?

I know that I should Respect my Family and Friends and my Teacher and the nice, kind and helpful people I meet.

I know that Respect is how I can show them just how *awesome* and *special* I think they are.

Best of all, by showing Respect to them means they will show Respect to **ME** too! This makes me very proud and helps me to be the **Best ME That I Can Be**!

Hello Readers! ... Leave a Review?

Amazon Reviews can make a huge difference
to the overall success of this Book.

If you enjoyed reading this Book as much as I have enjoyed
writing it, please take a few moments to leave a quick Review.

I would really appreciate it!

Thank YOU!

ROSE ANGEBRANDT

Made in the USA
Las Vegas, NV
12 March 2021